Religious Education
in the Classroom

TWO

Christianity
and
Other World Faiths

by
E. Freedman and J. Keys

Published by
Prim-Ed Publishing

2851
REV–03/04

Foreword

This series of books aims to provide teachers with a wide variety of activities which will support the Religious Education curriculum, whether Model 1 or Model 2 is being used. The materials will help develop knowledge and understanding of what it means to be a member of a faith community and how the teachings of these religions relate to shared human experience.

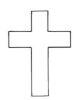

The activities were written to cover the attainment targets recommended for inclusion in an agreed syllabus.

Attainment Target 1: Learning about Religion

This includes the ability to:

- identify, name, describe and give accounts, in order to build a coherent picture of each religion;

- explain the meanings of religious language, stories and symbols; and

- explain similarities and differences between, and within, religions.

Attainment Target 2: Learning from Religion

This includes the ability to:

- give an informed and considered response to religious and moral issues;

- reflect on what might be learnt from religions in the light of one's own beliefs and experience; and

- identify and respond to questions of meaning within religions.

The materials aim to offer a coverage of the skills and processes in Religious Education, namely: investigation; interpretation; reflection; empathy; evaluation; analysis; synthesis; application; and expression. They can be used for whole class investigations and discussions, or by groups and pairs to engage in further research.

Fifty per cent of the activities within each book engage with Christianity; the remaining activities cover Buddhism, Hinduism, Islam, Judaism and Sikhism.

Contents

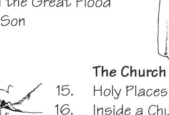

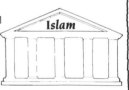
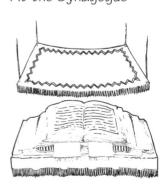

Teachers Notes

Christianity

1. and 2. Advent Calendar

Advent calendars are to help children focus on the lead up to the important event in the Christian calendar - the birth of Jesus Christ. In spite of the commercialism of this time it is still one of the most important times in the year for Christians.

Both sheets should be put onto cardboard if possible as this will ensure their survival through the month. It is important to remember that the doors on the first sheet should be cut out before it is stuck onto the back sheet.

The two sheets could be enlarged on a photocopier to give an A3 calendar which could be a class activity. The items in the boxes on the second sheet could be deleted and the children could draw their own objects, this would enable the items to follow a different theme.

3. Presents at Christmas

The quote is from Matthew 2. Discuss with the children their reasons for giving presents, and what they think about when choosing presents for others. It might be worthwhile to set a price limit, or to undertake the activity twice, once when money is no object.

4. Christmas Carols

It can be very useful to spend some time investigating the words of one of the carols, and to use one or more carols for language work at this time of year.

The history of carol singing can also be an interesting investigation for junior children.

5. Lent

Lent is the 40 days (excluding Sundays) before Easter. This is a time of preparation for the celebrations, and also a time of reflection. Children could be told the story of Jesus in the wilderness and they could talk about what it might have been like. Christians used to fast during Lent, as Jesus had spent the 40 days in the desert without food. Now they are asked to share in this memory by eating more simple food or giving up something.

Shrove Tuesday, or Pancake Day, was the day on which people were 'shriven', they confessed their sins and were forgiven. It was also a chance to eat some rich food prior to the fasting, and a way of using up these foods. There are many carnivals before the beginning of Lent, to celebrate before the fast.

6. and 7. Holy Week

Tell the class about the events of the last week of Jesus' life from the Gospels of Matthew, Ch.21 v.1-13 and Ch.26 v.17-29 and Luke Ch.21 v.1-4. Use a children's version. There is no reason why the children should not hear the whole story. Children may be unable to understand why Christians celebrate Easter time unless they are aware of the events of Holy Week and the first Easter.

The biblical references for each of the events are listed here:

Jesus rides into Jerusalem on a donkey. - Mark 11 / John 12

Jesus is arrested in the garden of Gethsemane. - Matthew 26 / John 18

Jesus tells the people to, 'give to Caesar what belongs to Caesar and give to God what belongs to God'. - Matthew 26 / Mark 12

Jesus carries his cross to Golgotha. Simon helps him. - Mark 15

The Jewish Sabbath is a day of rest.

Jesus tells Mary, 'tell my disciples that I have risen and that I am on my way to the one who is my Father'. - John 20

Peter denies Jesus three times. - Luke 22 / John 18

Jesus clears the traders from the temple. - Mark 11

Peter and John find a room for the Passover meal. - Mark 14

The women find the stone rolled back from the tomb. - John 20

Jesus is tried by Pilate. - Luke 23 / Mark 15

Jesus dies on the cross. - Mark 15 / Luke 23 / John 19

Judas Iscariot takes thirty pieces of silver to say where to find Jesus. - Matthew 26

The disciples find the tomb empty. - John 20

The crowds call for Jesus to be crucified. - Luke 23 / Mark 15

The people sing, 'God bless the one who comes in the name of the Lord'. - Mark 11 / John 12

Jesus taught his disciples how to break bread and drink from the cup, in memory of him. - John 13 / Mark 14

Teachers Notes

8. Christingle

The first Christingle service was held in Germany in 1747. The minister gave all the children Christingles to take home, and told them to put them in their windows for everyone to see. He wanted them to tell everyone what each of the parts stood for, and that Jesus was the Light of the World. The celebration was reinstated over 200 years later, in England by The Children's Society in 1976. The service is usually held around Christmas time, to thank God for his gifts, as this is the darkest time of the year in the Northern Hemisphere and Jesus, God's greatest gift to Christians, is the Light of the World.

9. Harvest Festival

Some Harvest Festivals are held at the beginning of Harvest, some at the end. Harvest festivals are held in the Autumn, between August and October in the Northern Hemisphere and March and May in the Southern Hemisphere. In Scotland and other Celtic countries, Lammas meaning 'loaf mass' is celebrated on 1 August.

It is an opportunity to discuss the produce from the local area, or the nearest growing area. Why do we celebrate the harvest? Do other cultures and religions celebrate the harvest? What effect can a bad or good harvest have? Was this more important in the past? Why do we give the produce away after the service? To whom does it go?

10. and 11. The Life of Jesus

The correct order of the events on these pages and their biblical references are:

Born in a stable	Luke 2; Matthew 2
Flight into Egypt	Matthew 2
Lost in the temple	Luke 2
Carpenter's Apprentice	(not in bible)
Baptised by John	Matthew 3
The Feast at Cana	John 2
Come with Me	Mark 1, 2 & 3
The Sermon on the Mount	Matthew 5; Luke 6
Awake from Death	Mark 5
Palm Sunday	Mark 11; John 12
Last Supper	Mark 14; John 13
Trial of Jesus	Mark 15; Luke 23
The Crucifixion	Mark 15; Luke 23; John 19
The Empty Tomb	John 20

It is important to note and discuss that there is nothing detailing Jesus growing up. It is important to leave space on the time line to show this time. The Feast at Cana was the first miracle and it was after this that Jesus started to preach.

12. People in the Bible

It will be worthwhile to discuss with children any of the people they know from the bible. It may be a good introduction to have children think of a character, write a two-sentence description of the character and then ask a partner or the class to guess who the character is. This will be a good introductory activity before children attempt the sheet. It might also be useful to encourage children to work in pairs, particularly if they do not have extensive knowledge of Biblical people. Either before or after the completion of the sheet, share the stories with the children. The people and some of the Bible references are:

Moses - The Book of Exodus

Queen of Sheba - First Book of Kings, Ch. 10

John the Baptist - Luke 1, Matthew 3, John 1 & 3

Peter, the Apostle - Mark 1, 2 & 3, John 21

Mary - Luke 1 & 2, Matthew 1, John 19

Jesus - Gospels and Acts of the Apostles

Teachers Notes

13. Noah and the Great Flood

It is important to read the story from the Bible and to discuss it with the class, before they complete the sheet. It might also be beneficial to discuss some of the things the class think might have been said in the circumstances, and why the two characters with speech balloons might say something very different, and also what other characters might say. The reasons for the speech is as important as the words.

Genesis 6 - 10

14. The Lost Son

Read the story as a class and discuss the issue. The discussion is very important and will help children to understand the lesson implicit in the text.

Luke 15

15. Holy Places

It is important children understand that Christianity has been part of Britain for a long time; also that it was brought to Britain by early holy men. Each of the four places marked on the map are associated with an early 'missionary' or teacher.

Iona - St Columbia,
Lindisfarne - St Cuthbert,
St David's - St David,
Canterbury - St Augustine

16. Inside a Church

It would be useful to take children to see a range of Christian churches so they can begin to understand how they are different, for example, a Catholic church from a Baptist chapel or an Orthodox church. This will also allow children to see the similarities and those sign symbols, artefacts and ceremonies which unite Christian churches. If this is not possible, use photographs of the various churches as props for discussion.

Children could be asked to write alternative descriptions of the objects or write descriptions of other objects and have their classmates name them. Those in the illustrations are: font; pews; altar; stained glass windows; lectern; statues; cross.

17. The Christian Year

It may be useful to undertake this sheet as a pair or group activity. The Christian Year does have two cycles within it, the Christmas and the Easter cycles. The Christmas cycle is solar and the Easter cycle is lunar. Therefore, children could concentrate on one or other of the cycles, and bring the information together. It is a good opportunity to look in more detail at some of the other celebrations in the Christian Year.

18. Celebration of Christian Life

The purpose of this sheet is to look at some of the rituals in Christian life.

Baptism is an initiation which welcomes a newcomer to the community of the church. This is usually undertaken in infancy but not always.

Confirmation is a ritual of 'confirming' the person as a member of the church. This is held at different times in various Christian faiths, it is usually preceded by instruction and is in part a 'coming of age' as a Christian.

Wedding is the ritual of joining two people together, as a separate family unit. Each church has a different view of the importance of this ceremony.

Sunday Service is an integral part of life as a Christian, it is the ongoing celebration of the faith and all Christians are encouraged to participate.

19. Christian Way of Life Wordsearch

The discussion surrounding the completion of this sheet will be very valuable.

Teachers Notes

20. Our Father Prayer

This is the prayer which Jesus gave to his disciples when they asked him how they should pray. Jesus said that when you pray you should not show off. You should find a place on your own and then talk to your Father, using simple words and this is the model he gave us. (Matthew 6; Luke 11)

Children can colour the pattern, cut out the prayer and keep their own copy.

You can discuss with the children what the words mean and why they have changed slightly. It is probably not helpful to analyse the praycr too thoroughly with young children, but you can do more analysis with older pupils. You could delete some of the words before photocopying and ask the children to fill them in.

21. Committed Christians - Saints

This sheet will encourage children to find out more about the saints listed and why they have become saints. Children could also research another saint, for example, one after whom they were named, a local saint or one about whom they have heard.

22. Followers of Jesus

The importance of this sheet is in the children understanding how people put Christianity into practice in their daily lives. All three of these people gave their lives to helping others, but there are other people who follow the teachings of Jesus in their daily lives in a more ordinary way. Children will be able to think of local examples once they have thought about how someone can help someone else.

It might be worthwhile to look at the last two worksheets before this one.

23. Caring and Sharing - A Quiz

These dilemmas are part of daily life, it is important that children have a chance to discuss their answers and that they do not feel inhibited in saying what they think. There could be a general discussion before the sheet is completed or afterwards which focuses on why children answered as they did. A discussion with a partner first could be less threatening for some children.

24. Caring and Sharing - A Survey

As with the quiz, it is the discussion surrounding this sheet which will be most valuable. Comparison and discussion with another group may also help children to understand the role of helping those less fortunate in a community.

World Religions

25. Rules

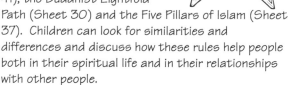

There are worksheets elsewhere in the book that set out the Judaeo-Christian Ten Commandments (Sheet 41), the Buddhist Eightfold Path (Sheet 30) and the Five Pillars of Islam (Sheet 37). Children can look for similarities and differences and discuss how these rules help people both in their spiritual life and in their relationships with other people.

If the school or class already have written rules then children can copy these out, otherwise this is an opportunity to formulate a set of rules that the children believe would help school life.

26. Holy Places

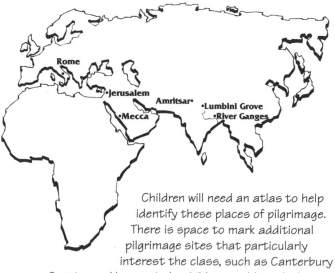

Children will need an atlas to help identify these places of pilgrimage. There is space to mark additional pilgrimage sites that particularly interest the class, such as Canterbury or Santiago. Alternatively, children could mark their home town.

Teachers Notes

27. Lifetimes

Most of the answers to these questions will be found in the other worksheets or children can use reference books for research.

Q: When a new baby is born ...?

a: A Muslim father whispers the call to prayer so that it is the first sound the baby hears.

Sikhs open their holy book at random and select a name that begins with the letter found at the top of the left hand page.

Many Christians make the sign of the cross with holy water on the baby's forehead.

Q: When a child is growing up ...?

a: Jews hold a Bar Mitzvah service at the synagogue when a boy reaches the age of thirteen, girls have their Bar Mitzvah at twelve.

Catholic Christians confirm girls and boys at around seven years of age.

Protestants do so when they are in their teens.

Hindus hold the Upanayam ceremony for a boy between the ages of eight and sixteen, when he starts to wear the Sacred Thread across his chest.

Q: When two people get married ...?

a: European Christians exchange rings.

Hindus tie her sari to his scarf.

Jews stand under a special canopy at the synagogue.

28. Greeting Cards

Making greeting cards is always a popular school activity. Here children are encouraged to identify important festivals from six major religions. As a follow-up activity they could make a card for one of these festivals based around the symbols shown on the worksheet.

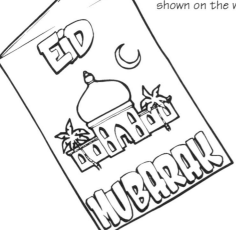

Buddhism

29. Life of Buddha

Before completing the worksheet children could read some of the many stories about the birth and early life of Buddha.

The four signs are usually portrayed as the key to his decision to leave home and follow a spiritual path.

30. The Wheel

The Eightfold Path that is taught to Buddhists may need some discussion before children can fully appreciate how these rules could be applied to modern school life.

31. Monks

If the class are studying English monastic life in History then they can compare this with modern Buddhist monks who also take vows of poverty, chastity and obedience.

32. Looking at Buddha

Images of Buddha hold a great many messages for believers. This worksheet explains some of the hand gestures used, children could look in reference books for other Buddha statues and work out their significance. Hand movements like this could also be explored in a drama lesson.

Hinduism

33. and 34. Rama and Sita

Before sorting out the pictures and text on these sheets children need to hear a version of the story of Rama and Sita which forms part of the ancient Ramayana.

35. A Hindu Temple

Children should, if possible, have an opportunity to visit a Hindu temple. Alternatively, there are many illustrated books on Hinduism showing both traditional Indian temples and British temples.

Teachers Notes

36. Krishna

Krishna is a much-loved Hindu God and there are many stories about him. He is often shown as blue because he once swallowed poison to save the world. The stories about Krishna and the milkmaids are connected with the Hindu veneration for the cow.

Islam

37. The Five Pillars of Islam

Encourage children to see the metaphor of these rules being the pillars that support Islam. They may like to make comparisons between these rules, the Buddhist rules and the Ten Commandments.

38. Muhammad at Mecca

The story of Muhammad's victory at Mecca in 630 CE (AD) is a surprising one. The people of Mecca had broken their peace treaty, attacking and killing a group of Muslims, yet when Muhammad and army marched on the city there was virtually no bloodshed, no reprisals and no looting of the city.

39. Ramadan

Muslims follow a lunar calendar so the month Ramadan does not have a fixed date in our calendar. According to the Koran only healthy adults should fast throughout Ramadan, but some Muslim children are encouraged to fast for a day or two.

40. At the Mosque

The mosque shown in the worksheet is typical of those seen in traditional Muslim countries but children in Britain may be more used to seeing other buildings that have been converted into mosques.

Judaism

41. The Ten Commandments

The full version of the Commandments is to be found in Chapter 20 of the Book of Exodus. Jews call this the Torah, Christians call it the Old Testament.

42. Moses

The story of the birth of Moses and how his mother hid him in the bulrushes, where he was found by Pharaoh's daughter and how he grew up and freed the Jews from slavery in Egypt, is told in the Book of Exodus.

43. The Passover Meal

This traditional Jewish festival is intended to teach children about the Exodus story. There is a special Seder plate holding:

- a roast lamb bone symbolising the Paschal lamb sacrificed in the Temple
- a hard-boiled egg symbolising the loss of the Temple in 70 CE
- parsley or similar leaves to dip into salt water symbolising the tears of the Jews
- haroset (a mixture of apple, nuts and wine) symbolising the mortar the slaves used when building
- bitter herbs such as horseradish to symbolise the bitter life of the slaves in Egypt.

At Passover Jews eat only unleavened bread (matzah) because when they left Egypt there was no time for bread with yeast to rise.

Teachers Notes

44. At the Synagogue

Although there are many differences between Orthodox, Reform and Liberal synagogues, all would agree on the central importance of the Torah scrolls.

Sikhism

45. The Holy Book

Sikhs consider their holy book to be the eleventh Guru and therefore all copies are treated with enormous respect. It will not be possible for children to see the book unless they are invited to visit a Sikh home or Gurdwara.

46. Helping Others

The simple moral of this story can be appreciated by children from all faiths. Guru Gobind Singh was the tenth Guru and founder of the Khalsa brotherhood. He led the Sikhs from 1675 to 1708 and fought many battles with the Muslim armies of the Emperor Aurangzeb.

47. Guru Nanak

Guru Nanak was the first Guru, or leader, of the Sikhs. He lived from 1469 to 1539 and there are many stories told about his life.

48. Gurpurbs

If the children are intrigued by the idea of people reading a book nonstop for forty-eight hours, they could try a reading marathon for themselves, then work out as a mathematics problem how long it would take them to read all 1,430 pages of the Guru Granth Sahib.

note:

When dealing with religions other than Christianity it is customary not to use BC and AD for dates. BCE (Before the Common Era) is used for BC and CE (Common Era) for AD.

Advent Calendar 1

☆ *Colour the picture and make the Advent Calendar.*

Advent Calendar 2

☆ Colour the pictures and glue this page behind Advent Calendar 1 to make your Advent Calendar.

☆ Colour the pictures and glue this page behind Advent Calendar 1 to make your Advent Calendar.

After Jesus was born three wise men came from the east to visit him. They each brought him a present.

The gifts were:

gold, fit for a king;

frankincense, sweet smelling incense offered in temples; and

Frankincense

myrrh, fragrant spice of anointing the dead.

Myrrh

At Christmas we give presents to our friends and family.

☆ *Think about three people you will give presents to this Christmas. Write their names on the box labels and write on the side of the box what you will give them.*

Lent

Fill in the spaces in this passage with the following words.

Word bank: preparation, pancakes, forty, water, Lent, Shrove Tuesday, Jesus, Ash Wednesday, forgiven

Easter is the most important festival in the Christian year. It has a period of preparation which is called Lent. Before a special holiday, we often prepare in a certain way. Christians have a special _____ for Easter. Lent is the _____ days before Easter, excluding Sundays. This is a time to remember the 40 days _____ spent in the desert without food or _____ . The day before Lent begins is called _____ _____ . We sometimes call it Pancake Day. This is because people used to give up milk, eggs and sugar during Lent, so they made pancakes before Lent began. They would also go to church and ask to be _____ (shriven) for their sins. Lent starts on _____ _____ . Some Christians put ash on their faces.

Many people fast during Lent, or give up something, to remind them of Jesus suffering. Write down what luxury or special food you would give up. Discuss your choices with a classmate.

_____

_____

_____

Christians believe that Easter is the triumph of life over death, of light over darkness. The resurrection of Jesus brings the promise of eternal life. Holy Week, from Palm Sunday to Easter Day is the most important week in the Christian calendar.

☆ *Here are some of the events which took place during Holy Week. Cut them out and glue them onto the diary on Holy Week 2.*

Jesus is arrested in the garden of Gethsemane.

Jesus rides into Jerusalem on a donkey.

Peter and John find a room for the Passover meal.

The women find the stone rolled back from the tomb.

The disciples find the tomb empty.

The crowds call for Jesus to be crucified.

Jesus washes the feet of his disciples.

Jesus carries his cross to Golgotha. Simon helps him.

Jesus clears the traders from the temple.

Judas Iscariot takes thirty pieces of silver to say where to find Jesus.

Jesus tells the people to, 'give to Caesar what belongs to Caesar and give to God what belongs to God'.

The people sing, 'God bless the one who comes in the name of the Lord'.

Jesus tells Mary, 'tell my disciples that I have risen and that I am on my way to the one who is my Father'.

Jesus taught his disciples how to break bread and drink from the cup in memory of him.

Peter denies Jesus three times.

Jesus is tried by Pilate.

The Jewish Sabbath is a day of rest.

Jesus dies on the cross.

Holy Week 2

Paste all of the labels from Holy Week 1 onto this page, on the days you think each event happened.

On Palm Sunday...

On Monday, Tuesday, Wednesday...

On Maundy Thursday...

On Good Friday...

On Saturday...

On Easter Sunday...

Christingle

The Christingle services are held in the lead up to Christmas. The Christingle is a Christian symbol of God's gifts to the world. The word 'Christingle' means 'Christ light'.

'At the Christingle service we have oranges and there are sweets stuck into them on sticks. We don't eat the sweets at the service, but we eat them afterwards. The lights are switched off so that the church is dark when the candles in the oranges are lit.' - John

At a Christingle service we all have a Christingle light.
To make a Christingle light you will need:
1 orange
4 cocktail sticks
sultanas, raisins, nuts and sweets
1 red ribbon
1 candle

☆ *Make your own Christingle light, like the one in the picture.*

The History of Christingle

The first Christingle service was held in Germany in 1747. The minister gave the children Christingles to take home and told them to put them in their windows. This would remind people that Jesus was the Light of the World. Over 200 years later in 1976, Christingles were brought to England by The Children's Society.

☆ *Each of the parts of the Christingle light stands for something.*
Match each thing with what it stands for.

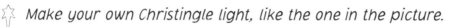

an orange •	• Jesus Christ, the Light of the World
4 cocktail sticks •	• God's love in sending Jesus to Earth
sultanas, nuts and sweets •	• the four seasons of the year
a red ribbon •	• the fruits of the earth
a candle •	• the world that God has created

Harvest Festival

At Harvest Festivals Christians thank God for all the good things which come from the Earth. Many things which are grown and harvested at this time are taken to the church to be blessed at the special services.

☆ *How many of the items in the drawing can you identify? Write what they are and use arrows to label them.*

☆ *Fill in the missing words in the passage below.*

grain   gifts   fruit   decorated   flowers   service   church   Autumn

The harvest of most grain and fruit is in _____ . The

Harvest Festival is celebrated during a _____ in

the church. It is to thank God for the _____ and the

_____ . At harvest time the _____ will be

_____ with _____ and

produce from the area. After the service the _____ will

be given to those in need.

The Life of Jesus 1

On this page and the next page you will find events from the Life of Jesus.
Make a timeline from 0 to 33. Jesus was 33 when he died.
Cut out the events on the two pages and glue them in the correct chronological order on
the timeline. This will tell you how old Jesus was when each event happened.

The Last Supper

The Feast at Cana

Flight into Egypt

Palm Sunday

Baptised by John

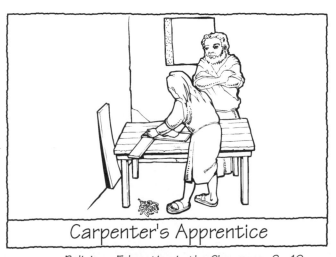

Carpenter's Apprentice

The Trial of Jesus

Sermon on the Mount

Born in a stable

The Empty Tomb

Awake from Death

The Crucifixion

Lost in the Temple

Come with Me

People in the Bible

Read the descriptions. Who are these people from the Bible?

He was born in Egypt. He was brought up by Pharaoh's daughter. He led his people to the promised land.

I am _____

She came to visit King Solomon because she had heard of his great wisdom. She ruled a foreign land but she brought valuable presents for Solomon.

I am _____

She was visited by God's angel Gabriel with great news. She married Joseph the carpenter. She saw her son die on the cross.

I am _____

He was born to elderly parents. He was chosen by God to prepare the people for the coming of the promised saviour.

I am _____

He was a fisherman in the Sea of Gallilee. When Jesus called, he followed. Jesus called him 'the rock' on which he would build his church.

I am _____

He was born in a stable in Bethlehem. He died on a hill outside Jerusalem 33 years later.

I am _____

The Lost Son

☆ Here is a story Jesus told. Read the story and draw your own pictures.

Jesus says we should love each other and forgive each other. How does this story tell us this?

_____

_____

_____

_____

_____

_____

_____

A farmer had two sons. One day the younger son asked for his share of the property so that he could leave home and seek his fortune in a foreign country. His father divided all he owned and the young man left home with his share of his father's property.

The young man spent his money recklessly and soon had no money left. There was famine where he was and everyone was poor. At last he found a job looking after pigs, he thought the pigs were better fed than he was. He decided to go back to his father and ask for a job.

His father saw him coming and ran to meet him. He kissed him and welcomed him. His son asked for his father's and God's forgiveness. His father then asked his servants to prepare clean clothes for him. Also to prepare a great feast to celebrate his son's return.

When the older brother heard of the feast he was furious and refused to go into the house. His father came out and asked him why. He was angry because he had worked hard for his father and never had a feast but his brother who had left and lost everything was having a celebration. His father said, 'My son you are always with me and you will inherit everything, but your brother was lost and now he is found'.

Holy Places

Historically, Britain was a place of pilgrimage.
A pilgrimage is a journey to a sacred place. Four sacred
places are shown on the map which are associated with
the coming of Christian teachers to Britain.

☆ *Find out the name of the teachers associated with each place.*

Iona _____

Canterbury _____

St David's _____

Lindisfarne _____

☆ *See if you can find out anything else about these teachers.*

☆ *Britain has many cathedrals celebrating Christian worship over many centuries.
Can you name the cities marked on the map which have great cathedrals?*

See if you can find out how old each cathedral is. Write them down in order of age.

*A cathedral is a place of worship. It is also a place to visit and a place where some
people work. Can you name the jobs of four people who work in a cathedral?*

Inside a Church

Churches are places where Christians meet to worship. As there are different Christian groups, they each have their own buildings for worship and they do not all look the same.

As all churches are Christian, they contain many things which are the same. Each type of Christian church will have things which are special to it and to the way they worship.

☆ *Here are some definitions of things you will find in churches.*
Can you name each one and draw a picture of it?

This is a special bowl which is used in baptisms. It is often beautifully carved. In earlier times it was sometimes in a separate building called a baptistery. In some churches it is near the main door, to show that baptism is the 'entry' to the church.

This is a special reading desk. The Bible usually sits on this. Some of the very old ones are in the shape of an eagle

These are found more often in older churches and larger churches. They were there to show people who could not read and write what the stories in the Bible said.

These are the symbols of Jesus Christ's death on the cross. They come in many different styles. Can you draw two different ones?

This is the most important part of most churches. It is usually at the east end of the building and may be made of stone or wood. The area around it is called the 'sanctuary', which means holy place. In Orthodox and Roman Catholic churches there is a special box nearby which contains the communion bread.

These are found mainly in Roman Catholic churches. Some older Anglican churches also have them. They are there because people think they help them worship. In Orthodox churches they have special pictures called icons.

The Christian Year

The Christian Year is a cycle throughout the year.
There are festivals and times which are significant.

☆ Here is a list of the main festivals, beginning with the Annunciation.
Match the description to the correct festival.

Annunciation

Christmas

Epiphany

Ash Wednesday

Palm Sunday

Maundy Thursday

Good Friday

Easter Sunday

Ascension

Pentecost

Jesus enters Jerusalem and is hailed a King.

The three kings celebrate finding the baby Jesus.

Jesus ascends into heaven.

Jesus is crucified.

Jesus celebrates the Last Supper with his disciples.

Jesus is born.

Jesus goes to the wilderness to pray.

Jesus rises from the dead.

The Holy Spirit is given to the disciples of Jesus.

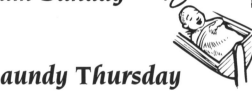

The angel Gabriel announces the coming birth of Jesus to Mary.

Celebrations of Christian Life

☆ Here are some ways in which Christians celebrate together.
Can you match the labels at the bottom of the page to the pictures?

Confirmation ●

Sunday Service ●

● Wedding

● Baptism

☆ Can you think of some other times when Christians celebrate together?

_____

_____

_____

_____

Christian Way of Life Wordsearch

Can you find all of the words listed below in the grid?

s	a	i	n	t	c	l	b	h	f
c	h	u	r	c	h	o	a	o	e
h	a	x	r	m	r	r	p	l	s
r	r	u	s	c	i	d	t	y	t
i	v	w	o	r	s	h	i	p	i
s	e	e	c	o	t	e	s	r	v
t	s	d	a	s	m	a	m	i	a
i	t	d	r	s	a	s	b	e	l
a	p	i	o	h	s	t	i	s	f
n	e	n	l	y	t	e	b	t	o
f	w	g	b	m	c	r	l	r	n
a	d	v	e	n	t	w	e	a	t

church	lord	hymn	worship	Christmas
festival	bible	carol	cross	Easter
font	advent	holy	wedding	baptism
harvest	saint	pew	Christian	priest

Our Father Prayer

Jesus told his disciples that they should pray using simple words and that they should mean what they said.

Here is the prayer that Jesus gave us. Colour the border.

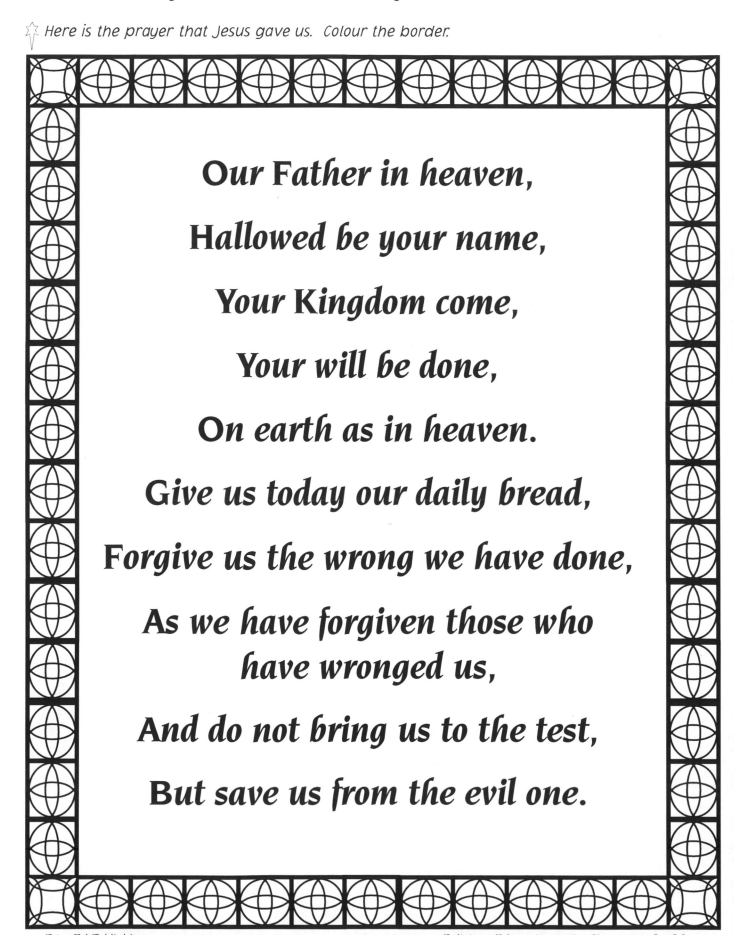

Our Father in heaven,

Hallowed be your name,

Your Kingdom come,

Your will be done,

On earth as in heaven.

Give us today our daily bread,

Forgive us the wrong we have done,

As we have forgiven those who have wronged us,

And do not bring us to the test,

But save us from the evil one.

Committed Christians - Saints

Throughout the history of the Christian faith, there have been many committed Christians who have become saints. Sometimes these Christians have been martyrs, people who were prepared to die rather than give up their belief in Jesus. Others have been important in spreading the words and beliefs of Christianity to others.

☆ *Here is a list of Christian saints. See if you can find out something about each of them, including why they might have become a saint.*

Saint Andrew the Apostle

_____
_____
_____
_____

Saint David

_____
_____
_____

Saint Francis of Assisi

_____
_____
_____

Saint Stephen

_____
_____
_____

Saint Joan

_____
_____
_____

Saint Hilda

_____
_____
_____

Saint Mary Magdalene

_____
_____
_____

Saint Patrick

_____
_____
_____

☆ *Some people are named after saints. See what you can find out about your saint's name, if you have one, or a friend's saint's name.*

Followers of Jesus

There are many Christian men and women who model their lives on the life of Jesus. They try to follow the things he told us through his teachings and they try to help others.

☆ Can you match the names of these people to their description?

● He was born in Belgium in 1840. He went to work in a mission in the Pacific Islands and became a priest. In 1865 he went to Malakai, where people who had leprosy (now known as Hensen's disease) were living. He lived and worked with these people for 16 years, until his death with the disease. He publicised the conditions in the colony and helped raise awareness of others.

● **Mary Verghese**

● She was born in 1925 in Kerala, South India. She studied medicine, but her career was cut short when she was injured in a car crash. The car crash left her paralysed in a wheelchair. Her faith helped her to accept being a paraplegic and she forgave the person who caused the car crash. Encouraged by Paul Brand she resumed her professional life and became a leading surgeon, working from a wheelchair. She worked tirelessly for paraplegics and for the people in Paul Brand's mission.

● **Mother Theresa**

● **Father Damien**

● She was born in 1910 in Albania. She began to work with the poor people in the slums of Calcutta after teaching in a girls school in the city. She set up a community of women to work with her. Her work continued for over seventy years and she has inspired many others to take up the care and concern for their fellow human beings. In 1979 she was awarded the Nobel Prize for Peace.

☆ Can you think of others who follow the gospels and are committed Christians? What do you think is important to do as a committed Christian?

Caring and Sharing - A Quiz

☆ *answer the questions in this quiz. Compare your answers with a partner.*

1. You help your neighbour in the garden.

   She gives you a box of chocolates. Do you,

   a. Give everyone in your family one chocolate each?

   b. Keep them in your bedroom and eat them yourself?

   c. Share the whole box with your family and friends?

   Why? _____

2. When you are walking home from school, you find a lost kitten. Do you,

   a. Walk on and leave it?   **b.** Take it home and keep it?

   c. Ring the RSPCA to see if they know who owns it?

   Why? _____

3. There is a new child in your school, who is in your class. At lunchtime do you,

   a. Ignore the child and play with your friends?

   b. Taunt the child and make them feel unhappy?

   c. Ask the child to join in your game?

   Why? _____

4. At lunchtime you find one of the children in your class crying in the playground.

   What do you think you should do?

   _____

   _____

   _____

   Why? _____

   _____

Caring and Sharing - A Survey

Fill out this survey, asking everyone in your class. You could repeat it with another class.

	Everyone in the class	Ten or more	A Few	Only one	No-one
Give money to those in need					
Do something to help someone in your family					
Do something for someone outside your family - in the community					
Help charities by buying something from them, such as Christmas cards					
Give your good old clothes or toys to others					

Rules

Many religions have rules to help people live a good life.

☆ *Fill in the names.*

_____

and _____ keep the

Ten Commandments.

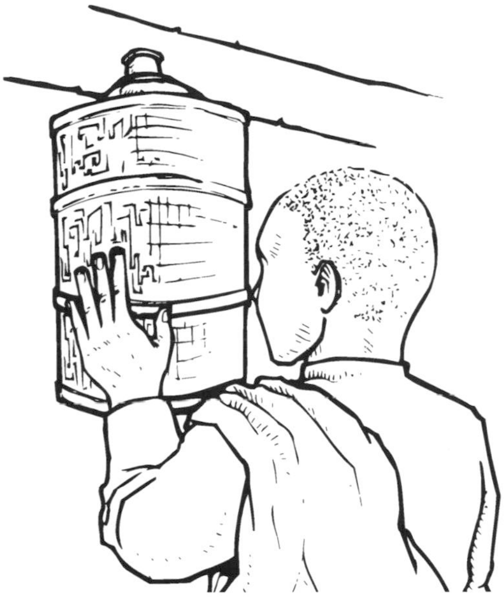

_____ honour the

Five Pillars of Islam.

_____ follow the eight-fold path.

☆ *What are the rules in your class?*

_____

_____

_____

_____

_____

_____

_____

_____

Holy Places

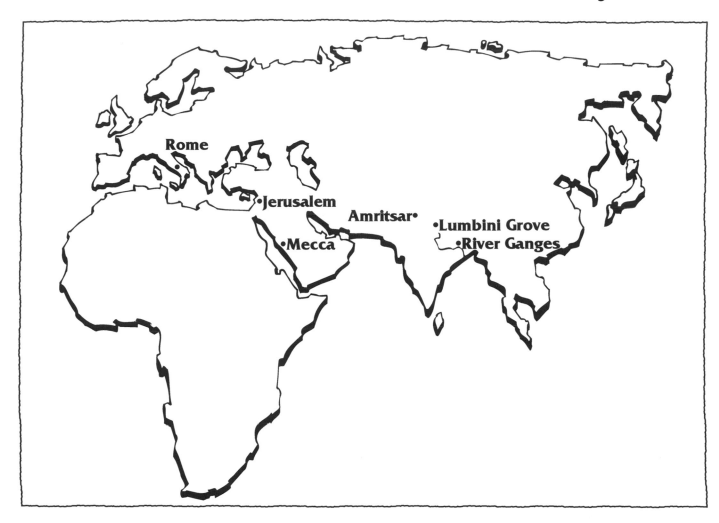

Rome

•Jerusalem

•Mecca

Amritsar•

•Lumbini Grove
•River Ganges

Many faiths have special places that people like to visit. We call these special journeys pilgrimages.

☆ *Look at the places marked on the map then complete the sentences.*

1. Hindu pilgrims go to the holy river _____ .

2. Buddhist pilgrims go to _____ _____ where Buddha was born.

3. Jewish pilgrims go to their holy city called _____ .

4. Sikh pilgrims go to the Golden Temple at _____ .

5. Muslim pilgrims go to _____ for the Hajj festival.

6. Catholic pilgrims go to _____ where the Pope lives.

Lifetimes

People in all religions want to celebrate the important changes in human lives.

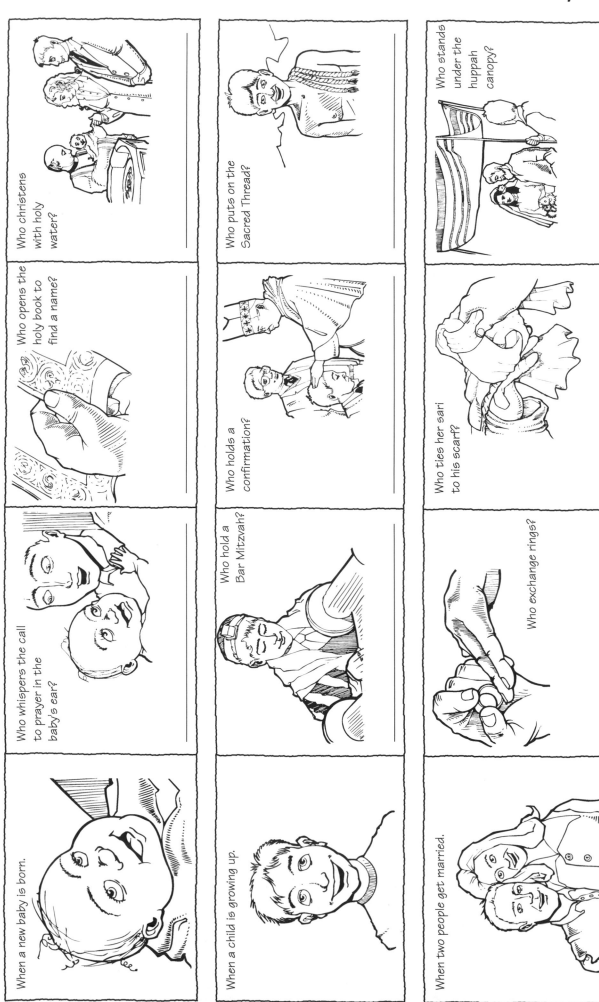

When a new baby is born.

Who whispers the call to prayer in the baby's ear?

Who opens the holy book to find a name?

Who christens with holy water?

When a child is growing up.

Who hold a Bar Mitzvah?

Who holds a confirmation?

Who puts on the Sacred Thread?

When two people get married.

Who exchange rings?

Who ties her sari to his scarf?

Who stands under the huppah canopy?

☆ Find out what different faiths do at these times.

HAPPY BAISAKHI

☆ Can you sort out which card to send for which festival? Write the answer and join it to the card.

BEST WISHES, FOR ROSH HASHANAH

GREETINGS AT VESAK.

The Muslim festival at the new moon which ends the Ramadan fast.

The full moon in May when buddhists celebrate the life of Buddha.

EID MUBARAK

MERRY CHRISTMAS

JANAMASHTAM GREETINGS

The Christian festival on December 25 that celebrates the birth of Jesus.

The summer festival when Hindus celebrate Krishna's birthday.

The festival on April 13 when Sikhs remember how Guru Goband Singh created the Khalsa.

The beginning of the Jewish New Year in September.

Life of Buddha

⭐ *Read the story, fill in the missing words from the list below and colour the pictures.*

Prince Siddhartha Gautama
was born long ago near the

_____
mountains.

A _____
said he could grow up to be
a great Emperor, but there were four
signs that he must never see.

The Prince grew up in a beautiful palace
where he never saw pain or sorrow.
One day he went out in his

_____ .

Outside the palace gate there was a

_____ man. Then an

_____ man went by. Then they

saw a _____ man.

Finally the Prince saw a holy man. Now he had

seen all the four _____ that
the fortune teller warned
his family to keep from him.

The Prince left his palace and went off to be a poor
wandering holy man. He became very wise and was

called the _____ .

chariot	**signs**
Buddha	**dead**
Himalayan	**sick**
fortune-teller	**old**

The Wheel

Buddhists use a wheel like this with eight spokes to remind them of the Eightfold Path - eight rules for living.

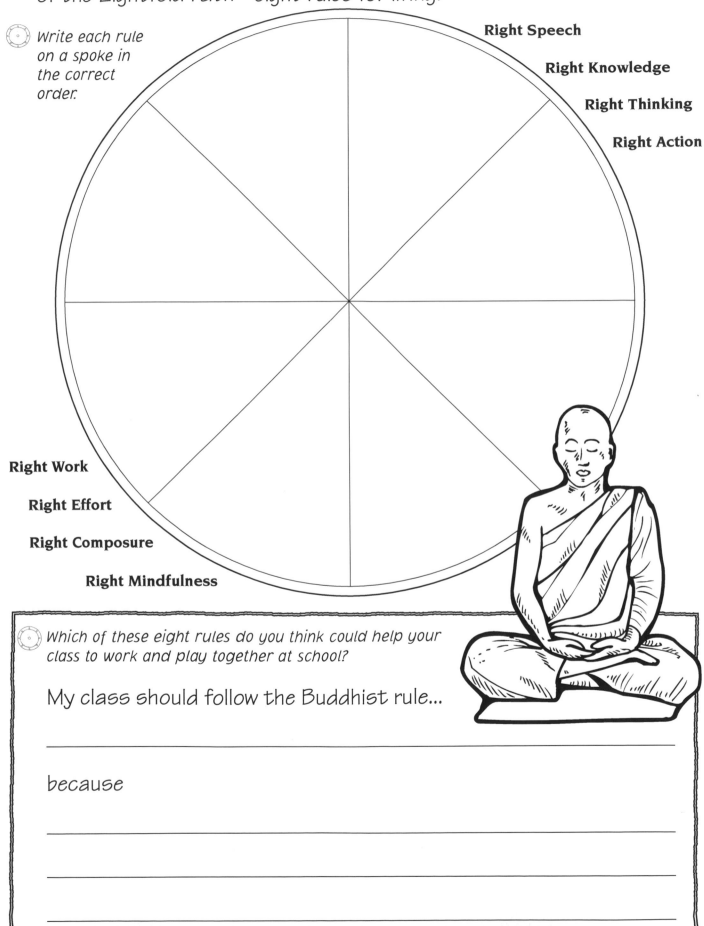

Write each rule on a spoke in the correct order.

Right Speech

Right Knowledge

Right Thinking

Right Action

Right Work

Right Effort

Right Composure

Right Mindfulness

Which of these eight rules do you think could help your class to work and play together at school?

My class should follow the Buddhist rule...

_____

because

_____

_____

_____

Monks

Label this picture of a Buddhist monk travelling in Sri Lanka. Notice how he has given up all his possessions to live a simple life as a holy man. He is carrying no bags and no money. He will ask other Buddhists to put food in his begging bowl.

| Shaved head | Begging bowl |

| Simple yellow robes | Umbrella |

Looking at Buddha

In Buddhist art the positions of Buddha's hands have a special meaning.

This picture shows Buddha touching the Earth as he did when he became enlightened.

Here Buddha is turning the wheel of the Law.

Here one hand is raised to protect, the other grants a wish.

Here Buddha is teaching.

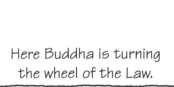 *Think about how we use our hands to give messages like these. Draw your own hands.*

Saying a prayer.

Waving goodbye.

Pointing the way.

Listen to the story of how Prince Rama rescued Sita from Ravana then put the pictures and text together in the correct order to make your own book.

The Story of Rama and Sita
from the
RAMAYANA

Cut out the text boxes and join each one to the correct picture then glue them onto a piece of paper to make a book.

The Story of Rama and Sita
from the
RAMAYANA

1. Long ago in India there was a Prince called Rama. He was the heir to the throne, but his cruel stepmother tricked his father so that he was banished for fourteen years. His beautiful wife Sita and his loyal brother Lakshmana went with him.

2. One day when Rama was living in the forest, he and his brother saw a magical golden deer. They followed it, and while they were gone the ten-headed demon Ravana kidnapped Sita and carried her away to his home in Sri Lanka.

3. Rama looked everywhere in the forest for Sita. At last Hanuman the Monkey King told him that it was the demon Ravana who had taken Sita to his island across the sea.

4. Hanuman and his monkeys all linked hands and made a bridge across the sea from India to Sri Lanka. Rama and Lakshmana hurried across the bridge. They found poor Sita a prisoner.

5. There was a great battle between Rama and Ravana. Hanuman set fire to the city with his tail. Rama used his magic bow. At last the demon was dead and Sita was safe.

6. Now the fourteen years were over, the prince and his friends could return to his kingdom. All the people were delighted to see them, they put lights in their windows to welcome Rama and Sita home.

A Hindu Temple

Fill in the missing words from the box below to find out about a visit to a Hindu temple.

India

statues

pictures

Hindu

mantras

flowers

door

bath

hands

arti

puja

food

Every town in _____ has a temple, which is a house for a

_____ God. There are many temples in Britain too. Inside

the temple there are brightly coloured _____ and

_____ of the gods. People _____ and put

on clean clothes before visiting the temple. They take off their

shoes at the _____ and bring gifts of _____

or _____ . Priests perform _____ and chant

_____ then everyone holds their _____

over the special _____ lamp.

Krishna

Hindus celebrate the birthday of Lord Krishna at Janamashtami. People put garlands of flowers on the statues of Krishna in the temple.

Hindus particularly like the stories about when Krishna was a cow herd and played on a flute to entertain the milkmaids.

Some people give lots of money to pay for decorations in the temple, but others are too poor.

In the *Bhagavadgita*, Krishna says:

'Whoever offers to Me a leaf, a flower, a fruit or water with devotion, I willingly accept, for it was love that made the offering.'

🕉 *Draw some things that anybody could offer to Krishna.*

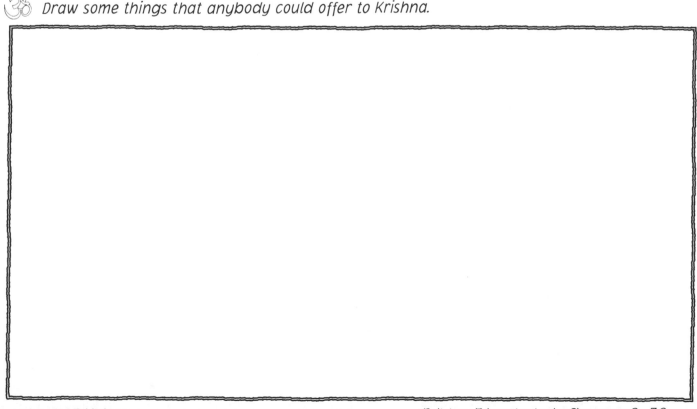

The Five Pillars of Islam

Shahada	Salat	Zakat	Sawm	Hajj
Say that you believe there is only one God - Allah and Muhammad is his prophet	Pray five times every day	Give money to the poor	Fast from sunrise to sunset in the month of Ramadan	Visit Mecca once in your lifetime

Islam

Pillars support a building, if one breaks the whole building may collapse. Muslims believe that keeping these five rules in their lives will support them in the same way.

Fill in the Arabic word for each rule. Write each name on one of the pillars above.

Muslims should do this once a year. _____

Muslims should do this every day. _____

Muslims should do this all the time. _____

Muslims should do this when they can afford it.

_____

Muslims should do this once in their lifetime.

_____

Muhammad at Mecca

☪ *Read the story about Muhammad, colour the pictures and answer the questions.*

In the year 630 CE Muhammad's army of 10,000 entered Mecca. People expected violence, but Muhammad made it a day of peace.

Muhammad opened the holy Ka'bah shrine of Abraham and threw the statues of false gods onto a fire.

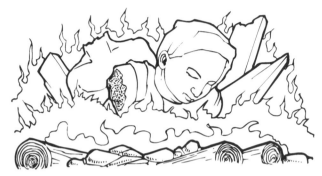

When the army of Mecca was defeated they expected to become slaves or lose their heads but Muhammad set them free.

After the battle Muhammad asked all his soldiers to kneel down and pray to Allah.

The people of Mecca expected war. What did Muhammad want?

_____

The people used to worship statues. Where did Muhammad put

them? _____

The soldiers of Mecca expected to die. What did Muhammad do?

_____

After battle some armies rob and kill. What did Muhammad's

soldiers do? _____

Ramadan

Read about Ramadan then find all the words highlighted in the wordsearch.

Ramadan is a special time for **Muslims**. It lasts for one **month**. Healthy adults **fast** during **daylight**. They eat breakfast before **dawn** and do not **eat** or **drink** again until the **iftar** meal when it is **dark**. They give money to help the **poor**. Ramadan ends with the **new moon** and then Muslim **families** celebrate with a feast called **Eid al Fitr**.

e	i	d	a	l	f	i	t	r
d	a	w	n	b	a	z	p	a
m	u	s	l	i	m	s	o	m
o	y	p	m	f	i	d	o	a
n	e	w	o	t	l	r	r	d
t	a	k	o	a	i	i	f	a
h	t	q	n	r	e	n	a	n
x	d	a	r	k	s	k	s	y
d	a	y	l	i	g	h	t	z

At the Mosque

☪ *Fill in the missing words in the passage below.*

Mosques often have a round roof called a _____ .

The tall tower called a _____ is used for the call to prayer.

You must take off your _____ when you enter a mosque.

People kneel on _____ _____ .

The wall that faces _____ is the qibla wall and everyone looks that way when they pray.

Muslims can say their daily prayers anywhere, but _____ is a holy day and everyone tries to be at the mosque for the _____ prayers.

| **Mecca** | **minaret** | **shoes** | **midday** |
| **Friday** | **dome** | **prayer mats** | |

The Ten Commandments

These are the laws that God gave to Moses. Jews and Christians try to live by these rules from the Bible.

1. You must have no other God but me.
2. Do not worship idols.
3. Do not use God's name lightly.
4. Do no work on the Sabbath day.
5. Respect your father and mother.
6. Do not murder.
7. Do not commit adultery.
8. Do not steal.
9. Do not tell lies against anyone.
10. Do not envy things that belong to someone else.

Some of these Commandments are part of our laws about how we treat other people. Some of them are about our duty to God.

Copy each of the Commandments into the correct box.

Our Duty to God

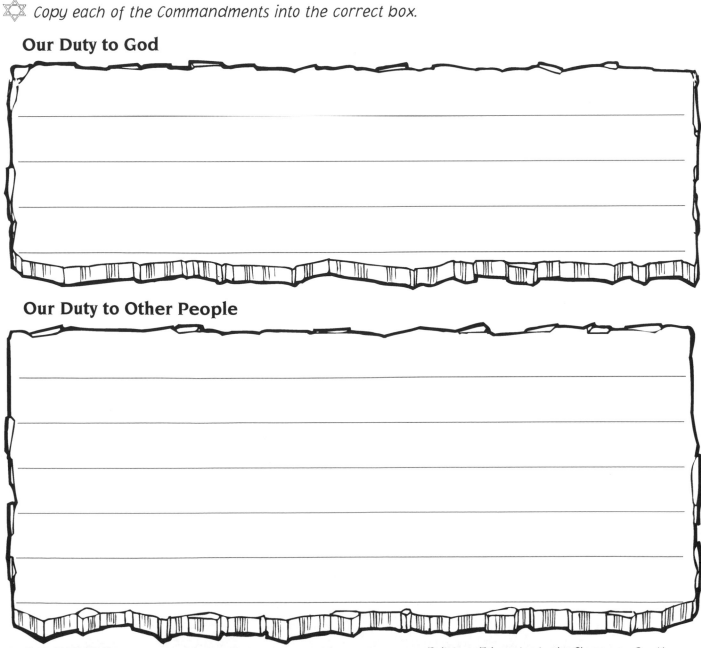

Our Duty to Other People

Moses

✡ *Read the story then draw a line to join each paragraph to the correct picture.*

Long ago the Jewish people from Israel were living in Egypt where they worked as slaves building the pyramids.

Moses asked the King of Egypt to let the people go back to their own land. Pharaoh refused, but then God punished the Egyptians until Pharaoh told the Israelites to go home.

God made a path through the Red Sea so the Israelites could cross safely. The Egyptians who followed them were drowned.

The people wandered in the desert for many years, living in tents with very little to eat. God sent them manna from heaven.

God spoke to Moses on top of a mountain called Sinai. He said the people must follow his Laws. Moses wrote out the Laws on two tablets of stone.

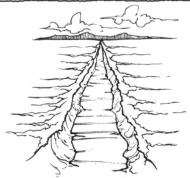

Before he died, Moses saw the Promised Land from the mountain top, but it was Joshua who led the Jewish people home from Egypt to Israel.

The Passover Meal

Every year at Passover, Jewish families eat a special Seder meal when they remember how God helped the Jews to escape from Egypt.

matzah

✡ *Fill in the missing words.*

The youngest child asks,

'Why is this night different from all other nights?'

The adults explain to the children,

'We eat _____ _____ to remind us how bitter life was for the Jewish slaves in Egypt.'

'We dip leaves in _____ _____ to remind us of the tears the slaves wept in Egypt.'

'We eat _____ to remind us that the Jews left Egypt in such a hurry there was no time for ordinary bread to rise.'

At the Synagogue

Fill in the missing words from the box below.

Jews go to

_____ on

_____ to pray and

listen to the _____

reading from the _____ .

This is never printed but always _____

_____ , not in a book but on a _____ .

A Torah scroll is always handled very _____

and kept in a beautiful velvet cover inside a special cupboard called

the _____ .

Synagogue	Shabbat	Rabbi	Torah
hand written	scroll	carefully	Ark

The Holy Book

The Sikh religion was founded over five hundred years ago by Guru Nanak (Guru means a holy man). Nine more Gurus followed, but when the tenth Guru died, he told the Sikhs there would be no more Gurus. Instead, their teacher would be the holy book - the Guru Granth Sahib.

The Guru Granth Sahib has 1,430 pages and contains 5,894 shabads or religious songs, written in the Punjabi language using Gurmukhi script.

The Guru Granth Sahib is always treated with great respect, as if it were a very important person. The book is kept in its own special room at the Gurdwara or at home. When Sikhs enter the room they take off their shoes and cover their heads. If the book has to be moved from place to place it is carried very carefully on someone's head.

See how the Guru Granth Sahib is treated like a King. Colour the pictures.

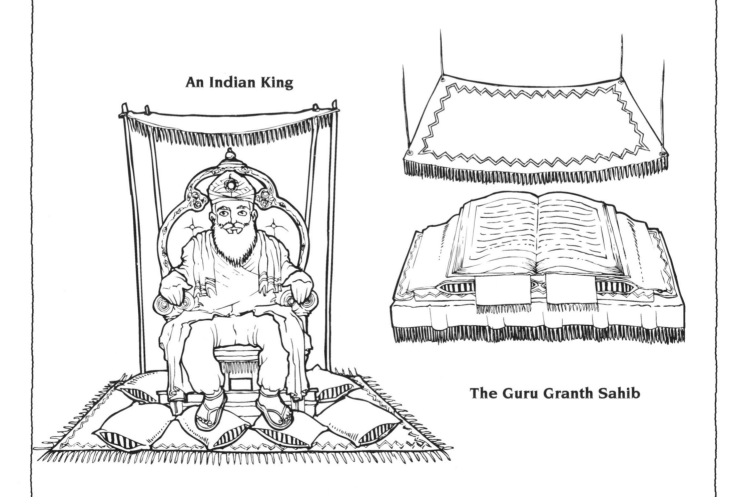

An Indian King

The Guru Granth Sahib

Helping Others

Sikhs show their faith by service to other people. This is called sewa and it is an important part of being a Sikh.

Guru Gobind Singh and his men fought a battle with the Emperor's army. After the battle many lay wounded. It was very hot.

🔱 *Read this story and draw your own pictures. You can show the Guru and the other Sikhs with beards and turbans. The Emperor's soldiers wore helmets and had no beards.*

Soldiers complained to the Guru that Ghanaya was giving water to wounded enemies as well as to the men on his own side.

When the Guru asked him, Ghanaya said it was true, he saw the Guru in every dying man, Sikh or non-Sikh, and tried to help them all.

Guru Gobind Singh praised Ghanaya for his kindness and gave him ointment for the wounded. Sikhs should always help others.

Guru Nanak

Lalor was a poor man who worked hard to buy food for his family. He invited Guru Nanak to eat with him.

Malik was a rich businessman who took money from the poor and treated them cruelly. He also invited Guru Nanak to dinner.

Guru Nanak chose to eat with Lalo. Malik was angry. The Guru took some bread from Lalo's house and some bread from Malik's. When he squeezed Lalo's bread drops of milk came out, from Malik's came blood.

Gurpurbs

Fill in the missing words to find out about Sikh festivals.

karah prashad **Guru Granth Sahib** **Akhand Path**

Gurdwara **forty-eight**

readers **birthdays**

parades **India**

carried **two**

Sikhs celebrate the b_____ of their Gurs

with an A_____ P_____ , a non-stop reading

of their holy book called the G_____ G_____

S_____ .

The granthis or r_____ take it in turns to read

for about t_____ hours each.

It takes about f_____ hours to read all

1,430 pages. Everyone who come to the

G_____ to listen is given k _____

p_____ , special food.

In I_____ there are special p_____ on

Gurpurbs when the holy book is c_____ through

the streets.

Answers

Page 4   **Christmas Carols**

bed, head, stars, hay.
Angel, shepherds, sheep, night, King.
three, mountain, star, light.

Page 5   **Easter**

preparation, forty, Jesus, water, Shrove
Tuesday, forgiven, Ash Wednesday.

Page 7   **Holy Week 2**

ON PALM SUNDAY....:
• Jesus rides into Jerusalem on a ....
• The people sing, 'God bless the ......
ON MONDAY, TUESDAY, WEDNESDAY......:
• Jesus clears the traders from the.......
• Jesus tells the people to, 'give to ......
• Judas Iscariot takes thirty pieces of ...
ON MAUNDY THURSDAY....:
• Jesus is arrested in the garden of .....
• Jesus washes the feet of his disciples.
• Peter and John find a room for the ..
• Jesus taught his disciples how to .....
ON GOOD FRIDAY....:
• Jesus carries his cross to Golgotha....
• Peter denies Jesus three times.
• The crowds call for Jesus to be ....
• Jesus is tried by Pilate.
• Jesus dies on the cross.
ON SATURDAY.....:
• The Jewish Sabbath is a day of rest.
ON EASTER SUNDAY.....:
• Jesus tells Mary, 'tell my disciples ......
• The women find the stone rolled .....
• The disciples find the tomb empty.

Page 8   **Christingle**

An orange – the world that God has created.
4 cocktail sticks – the four seasons of the
year.
Sultanas, nuts and sweets – the fruits of the
earth.
Red ribbon – God's love in sending Jesus to
Earth.
Candle – Jesus Christ, the Light of the World.

Page 9   **Harvest Festival**

Autumn, service, fruit, grain, church,
decorated, flowers, gifts.

Page 10   **The Life of Jesus**

Born in a stable, Flight into Egypt, Lost in the
Temple, Carpenter's Apprentice, Baptised by
John, The Feast at Cana, Come with Me, The
Sermon on the Mount, Awake from Death,
Palm Sunday, Last Supper, Trial of Jesus, The
Crucifixion, The Empty Tomb.

Page 12   **People in the Bible**

Moses, Queen of Sheba, Mary, John the
Baptist, Peter, Jesus.

Page 15   **Holy Places**

Iona–St Columbia, Canterbury–St Augustine,
St David's–St David, Lindisfarne–St Cuthbert.
Left side of map: Iona, St. David's, Wells,
Exeter.
Right side of map: Lindisfarne, Lincoln,
Peterborough, Norwich, Ely, Westminster
Abbey, Canterbury.

Page 16   **Inside a Church**

lectern, font, stained glass windows, altar,
cross, statues.

Page 17   **The Christian Year**

Annunciation–The Angel Gabriel announces
the coming birth of Jesus to Mary.
Christmas–Jesus is born.
Epiphany–The three Kings celebrate finding
the baby Jesus.
Ash Wednesday–Jesus goes to the wilderness
to pray.
Palm Sunday–Jesus enters Jerusalem and is
hailed a King.
Maundy Thursday–Jesus celebrates the Last
Supper with his disciples.
Good Friday–Jesus is crucified.
Easter Sunday–Jesus rises from the dead.
Ascension–Jesus ascends into heaven.
Pentecost–The Holy Spirit is given to the
disciples of Jesus.

Page 18   **Celebrations of Christian Life**

Baptism, Confirmation, Wedding, Sunday
Service.

Page 19   **Christian Way of Life Wordsearch**

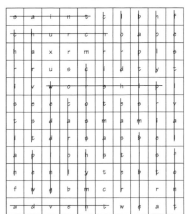

Answers

Page 22 Followers of Jesus
Father Damien, Mary Verghese, Mother Theresa.

Page 25 Rules
Ten Commandments: Jews and Christians.
Eight-fold Path: Buddhists.
Five Pillars of Islam: Muslims.

Page 26 Holy Places
1. River Ganges   2. Lumbini Grove
3. Jerusalem   4. Amritsar
5. Mecca   6. Rome

Page 28 Greeting Cards
- Muslim festival: Eid-Ul-Fitr.
- Full moon: Vesak.
- December 25th: Christmas.
- Krishna's Birthday: Janamashtam.
- April 13th: Baisakhi.
- Jewish New Year: Rosh Hashanah.

Page 29 Life of Buddha
Left to right: Himalayan, fortune-teller, chariot, sick, old, dead, signs, Buddha.

Page 30 The Wheel
Right Knowledge, Right Thinking, Right Speech, Right Action, Right Work, Right Effort, Right Mindfulness, Right Composure.

Page 31 Monks
Umbrella, Shaved head, Simple yellow robes, Begging bowl.

Page 35 A Hindu Temple
India, Hindu, statues, pictures, bath, door, flowers, food, puja, mantras, hands, arti.

Page 37 The Five Pillars of Islam
Sawm, Salat, Shahada, Zakat, Hajj.

Page 38 Muhammad at Mecca
Peace, onto a fire, set them free, knelt down and prayed to Allah.

Page 39 Ramadan

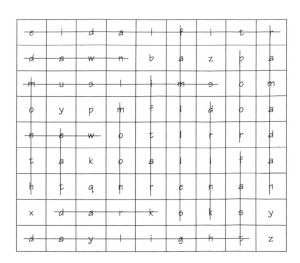

e	i	d	a	l	f	i	t	
d	a	w	n	b	a	z	b	a
m	u	s	l		m	s	b	m
o	y	p	m	f		d	b	a
h	b	w	o	t	l	r	r	d
t	a	k	o	a	i	i	f	a
h	t	q	h	r	e	n	a	h
x	d	a	r	k	s	k	s	y
d	a	y	l	i	g	h	t	z

Page 40 At the Mosque
dome, minaret, shoes, prayer mats, Mecca, Friday, midday.

Page 41 The Ten Commandments
Our Duty to God – Commandments 1–4.
Our Duty to other People – Commandments 5–10.

Page 43 The Passover Meal
bitter herbs, salt water, matzah.

Page 44 At the Synagogue
Synagogue, Shabbat, Rabbi, Torah, hand written, scroll, carefully, Ark.

Page 48 Gurpurbs
birthdays, Akhand Path, Guru Granth Sahib, readers, two, forty–eight, Gurdwara, karah prashad, India, parades, carried.